# LEGO® Friends Official Annual 2015

## Contents

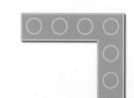

# Favourite Things

Everyone has things that they like to do best.
Read about the activities of the friends from Heartlake City
and match the descriptions to the right girl by writing
the number of the correct picture in the heart.
The words in bold should give you some handy hints...

Stephanie

1

I'm happiest when I'm performing on stage, even though I get nervous sometimes. One time, while performing at the Heartlake High assembly, I got so nervous that I ended up **singing** the wrong words to our school anthem!

3

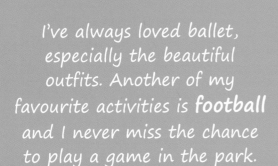

I've always loved ballet, especially the beautiful outfits. Another of my favourite activities is **football** and I never miss the chance to play a game in the park.

Olivia

2

## Andrea

**3**

5

One of my favourite things to do is play practical jokes on my friends and family! Once I put on a **red wig** and pretended to be Mia's long-lost cousin. I wish you could have seen everyone's face when they saw us together!

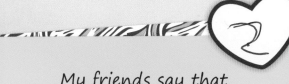

My friends say that I'm great at mending things, and my **screwdriver** can come in handy if we find ourselves in a sticky situation. Recently I saved Andrea's concert when the speaker broke. I managed to fix it in the blink of an eye!

## Mia

**4**

I love animals and have always liked spending time at the stables with the horses. But sometimes I can't resist taking one of the **apples** and eating it! Though I always feel a bit guilty afterwards...

4

## Emma

**5**

# Fabulous Photo Book

Follow this step-by-step guide to create a beautiful mini photo book. It's a great way to carry around all of your favourite photos!

## You will need:

❁ An A4 sheet of coloured card
❁ A pencil, a ruler, a pair of scissors
❁ Some glue
❁ 50cm of coloured ribbon
❁ Felt-tip pens, stickers and other things to decorate your photo book

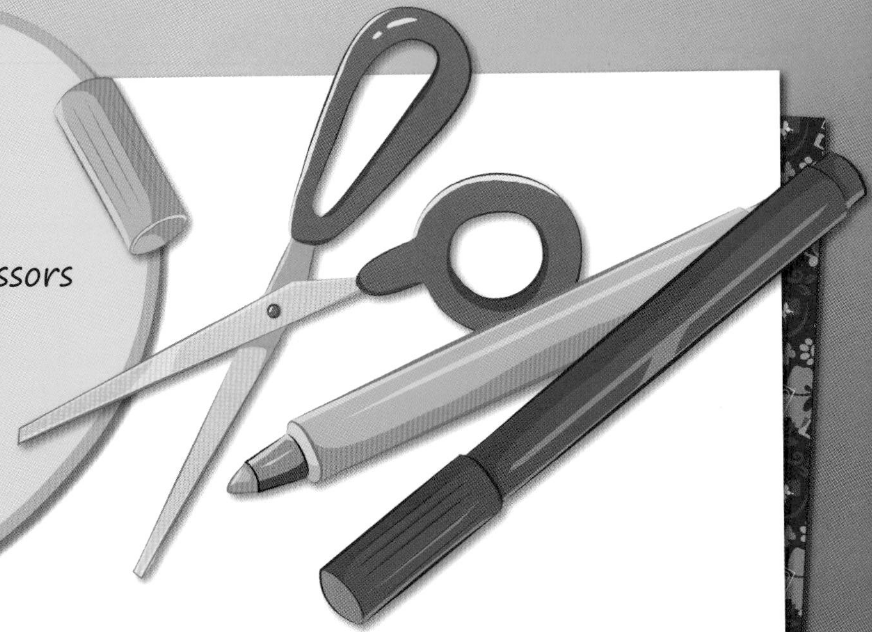

**1**

Cut a 7.5 x 29.5cm strip out of the sheet of coloured card.

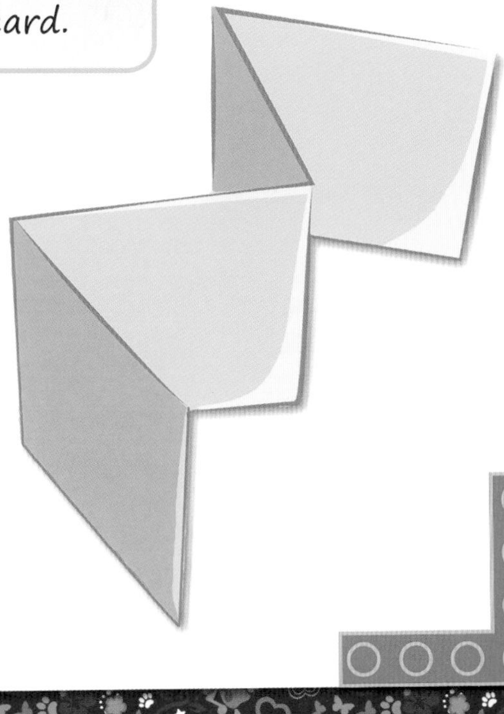

**2**

Fold the strip in half and then in half again to make a square. Now, unfold the strip and make a concertina, folding the paper as shown in the picture.

8

**3**

The squares at the front and back of the concertina will be the covers of your photo book. If you want, you can stick an extra piece of paper onto the covers to make them thicker.

**4**

Use glue to attach a ribbon to the back cover. Make sure the ends of the ribbon sticking out of both sides are the same length.

**5**

Now you can decorate the cover! Use coloured felt-tip pens, stickers or pictures cut out from old magazines to make it look beautiful.

More instructions on the next page . . .

**6**

The next step is to choose your favourite photos. Ask an adult to help you print some photos that will fit into the photo book.

**7**

Stick the photos into the pages of your photo book. If you want, you can decorate them to give your book an extra special look.

If you like
the mini photo book
you've created,
you can make
a few more!

 Stick some photos of you and your best friend in the photo book and give it to your friend as a gift.

 Choose some favourite family photos, stick them into your photo book and write about your best memories with your familiy on the following pages.

 Instead of photos, you could stick in some souvenirs from different events, e.g. a cinema ticket or a dried flower – to remind you of happy memories!

# Working Together

When friends work together, anything is possible!
Number these pictures in the right order, so that they
make an exciting story. Don't forget about the happy ending!

13

# Daydream Doodles

Sometimes when Emma is daydreaming,
she starts scribbling in her notebook without even
realising! Finish the doodles Emma has started by
repeating her patterns, or draw something completely new!

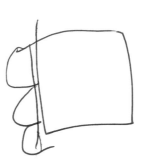

# Dolphin Quiz

Andrea loves being in the water with the dolphins. Take the quiz below to test your knowledge of these graceful animals. Write a 'T' next to the true sentences and an 'F' next to the false ones.

**F** Dolphins are big fish that live in rivers.

**T** They are exceptionally intelligent creatures.

**T** While sleeping, dolphins keep one eye open.

**F** Dolphins don't like to play.

**T** They speak a special 'dolphin language'.

**F** Dolphins are not very sociable so they prefer to stay away from people.

**T** Dolphins are usually very friendly.

# Even Number Path

Andrea is late to meet up with her friends and needs help finding her way through the grid! Can you draw a line from Start to Finish, going through only the even numbers, in a sequence that goes up by two with each step?

| 1 | 9 | 15 | 28 | 30 FINISH |
|---|---|----|----|----|
| 7 | 10 | 12 | 26 | 24 |
| 5 | 8 | 14 | 20 | 22 |
| 3 | 6 | 16 | 18 | 27 |
| 2 START | 4 | 5 | 29 | 25 |

# Ribbon Jumble

Emma loves to tie ribbons in her hair.
Count up how many ribbons are in the jumble below,
then write your answer in the heart!

Answer:

# Mirror Image

Try to spot the seven differences between these pictures.
To make it a little bit harder, the picture on the right side
has been flipped and is a mirror image of the picture on the left!

23

# The Best Friend Code

Are you a good friend?
Read these five important rules that best friends
should always try to keep in mind.

### Be a reliable friend.

Try not to let your friends down. For example, if you make plans with your friends, make sure you stick to them and avoid cancelling at the last minute!

### Listen to each other's problems.

Sometimes, your friends might need somebody to talk to. Try to be there to listen to their problems and worries.

### Be honest and open.

Don't be afraid to tell your friends how you really feel. If the truth is hard for them to hear, try to be gentle in how you tell it.

### Never gossip about your friends!

Even if you've had a fight with your friend and you feel angry with them, don't ever talk about them behind their back!

### Be there for each other.

There is nothing worse than being without your best friend when you need them. That's why you should always try and be there for your friends when they need your support.

# Diamond Dilemma

Emma has made a beautiful necklace out of diamonds.
All four of her friends' faces should be reflected on each gem,
but it looks like one of the girls is missing from each one.
Can you work out which girl needs to be added to each
diamond and draw a line to connect them?

# Animal Sketch

Mia loves taking care of forest animals.
Recently, she has made friends with a little fawn.
Follow this step-by-step guide to learn how to draw
the face of this cute baby deer!

5

6

7

27

# Photo Fun

Here are a few photos of the Heartlake City friends.
See if you can spot the two identical pictures below
and colour the hearts next to them in red.

# Spot the Sail Pattern

Look at Stephanie's windsurfing sail! Isn't it cool? Now look at the next page and see if you can spot the pattern on Steph's sail in the grid. Here's a clue: it appears vertically!

30

# Kite Chaos

Oh no! The strings of the kites have got tangled in a strong gust of wind. Follow the lines to work out which kite belongs to which girl. Can you spot which kite doesn't have an owner?

# Photo Jigsaw

Here's a picture of all the friends together!
Look at the next page and tick the flowers next
to the five jigsaw pieces that will complete the puzzle.

# The Autumn Apple Festival

The Annual Autumn Apple Festival will take place soon in Heartlake City. Use pencils and felt-tip pens to design a poster announcing this special occasion.

The
Autumn
Apple
Festival

# Category Match

Olivia is playing a matching game! The pictures below fit in one of the five categories on the screen. Help Olivia by writing the number of the matching pictures in the white boxes. Make sure you connect the right picture to the right category!

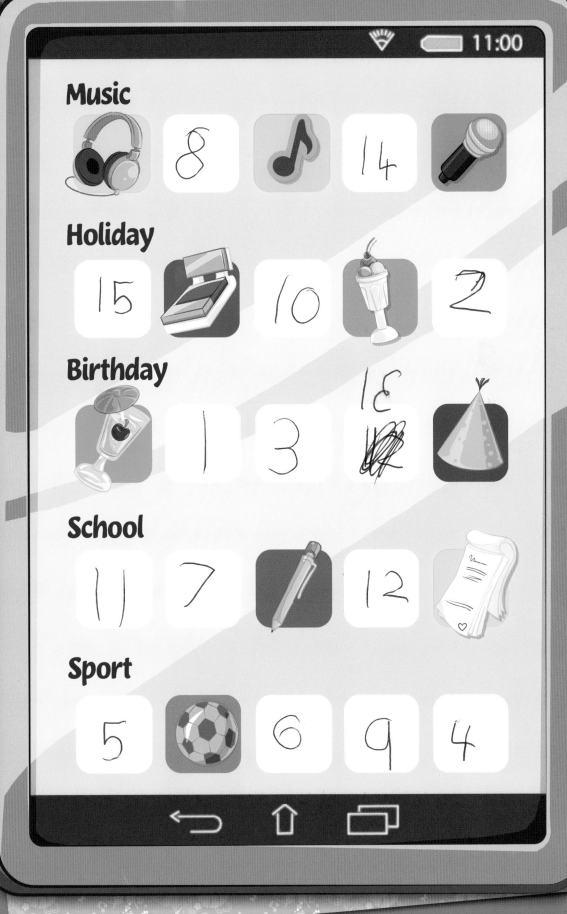

# Mixed-Up Picture

Today Olivia is working at the fruit and vegetable stall.
Can you arrange the sections of the picture on the right
in the correct order to match the picture below?
Write numbers in the stars to show which order the pictures go in.

# Magic 3D Drawing

Follow this step-by-step guide to create a 3D picture of your hand! All you need is a piece of paper and some coloured pens. Then just follow the steps shown in the pictures below! Once you've perfected this, you can use this technique to draw lots of different objects.

1

2

43

# A Quiet Trip

This weekend is going to be great!

And quiet!

I know, I love coming out to the ranch. It's so peaceful here!

I've got an idea for a project. I'm going to record all the sounds of the ranch!

You mean the silence?

**Some time later . . .**

Girls, come and look! Our mare has had a foal!

It's never seemed very noisy to me!

Wow, sounds amazing – I can't wait to see!

Aw, it's so cute!

Neigh, neigh . . .

meow . . .

45

# Crazy Curly Cards

Emma loves making beautiful cards for her friends.
Follow this step-by-step guide and use cute curls
to decorate a card for a special friend of your own!

## You'll need:

- An A4 sheet of coloured card

- Coloured paper cut into long 0.5 cm
  wide strips or special quilling strips
  (you can usually buy these in any arts
  and crafts shop)

- Some glue

 **1** Fold the A4 sheet in half, so that it looks like the card on the opposite page. This will be the base of your card!

**2** Choose flowers which you'd like to use to decorate your card. Think of the shape of the petals, the leaves, the stem and the colours. Look for inspiration on the next page!

**3** Now it's time for rolling! Take the first strip and start rolling it in your fingers as if you were making a snail's shell.

**4** Remember that the tighter you roll the paper the smaller the shape will be. If you want a bigger shape you can loosen the coil slightly. Once you've finished, glue the end of the quilling strip to the coil and pinch the edges to create whatever shape you wish.

**5** Put all coils on front of the card and arrange them in a nice pattern. Before you start to glue them down, check if you really like the design. If not, this is your last chance to change it.

**6** Apply glue under each coil and stick all the pieces onto your card. Be careful not to press down too hard, otherwise you may squash them. Now wait for the glue to dry – and it's ready!

# Beach Scene

The girls are spending their day at the beach. Can you spot all the objects in the list below? Count how many times each object appears and then write the number in the flower shapes.

# Fashion Sudoku

Andrea and Olivia are out shopping, but some of the objects have fallen off the shelves. Can you find the right place for each item? Draw a line to connect each object to its correct box. Remember that a hat, shoes and a handbag can only appear once in each row and column.

# Hot or Not!

Everyone has great fun with their friends!
Below is a list of activities you might like to do with your friends.
If you love the activity colour the star next to it in purple,
and if you don't like it colour the star in yellow.

| | | | |
|---|---|---|---|
| Playing board games |  |  | Playing computer games |
| Singing karaoke |  |  | Listening to music |
| Going to the cinema |  |  | Going to the funfair |
| Taking photos |  |  | Looking at photos |
| Fancy dress parties |  |  | Sleepovers |
| Relaxing on the beach |  |  | Playing sports |
| Watching TV |  | | Chatting about your favourite actors |

51

# Sunshine Ranch

It's a beautiful day on Mia's Sunshine Ranch. Look at the objects in the yellow and blue boxes, and try to find them in the picture. Be careful, though – not all of them are there!

# Lost in Books

It's easy to get lost in Heartlake City's beautiful library. Can you help Olivia find her way to the reading room? The correct path is only marked with blue books.

START

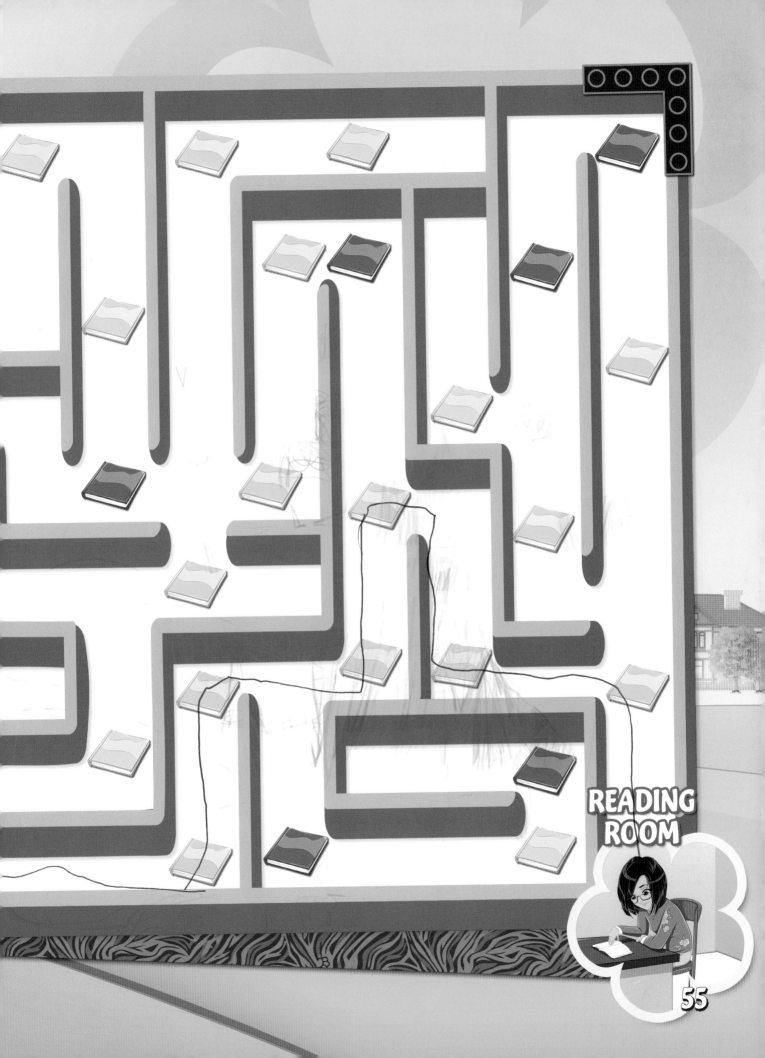

READING
ROOM

55

# Divine Designs

Emma and Andrea need a new handbag and necklace.
Pick an occasion from the list of three in each heart
and then design a new accessory just for them!

√ School
√ Theatre
√ Birthday party

Andrea's handbag

Cinema

✓ Shop

✓ Picnic

Emma's necklace

# Gorgeous Gown

Now you've helped Emma and Andrea with their outfits, it's time to design your very own! Use coloured felt-tip pens to design a beautiful dress for yourself.

# Answers

## p. 2-3

 Stephanie
 Olivia
 Andrea
 Mia
 Emma

**1** I've always loved ballet, especially the beautiful outfits. Another of my favourite activities is **football** and I never miss the chance to play a game in the park.

**2** My friends say that I'm great at mending things, and my **screwdriver** can come in handy if we find ourselves in a sticky situation. Recently I saved Andrea's concert, when the speaker broke. I managed to fix it in the blink of an eye!

**3** I'm happiest when I'm performing on stage, even though I get nervous sometimes. One time, while performing at the Heartlake High assembly, I got so nervous that I ended up **singing** the wrong words to our school anthem!

**4** I love animals and have always liked spending time at the stables with the horses. But sometimes I can't resist taking one of the **apples** and eating it! Though I always feel a bit guilty afterwards...

**5** One of my favourite things to do is play practical jokes on my friends and family! Once I put on a **red wig** and pretended to be Mia's long-lost cousin. I wish you could have seen everyone's face when they saw us together!

## p. 16-17

| F | Dolphins are big fish that live in rivers. |
| T | They are exceptionally intelligent creatures. |
| T | While sleeping, dolphins keep one eye open. |
| F | Dolphins don't like to play. |
| F | They speak a special 'dolphin language'! |
| F | Dolphins are not very sociable so they prefer to stay away from people. |
| T | Dolphins are really friendly. |

## p. 20

## p. 21

## p. 22-23

## p. 25

59

**p. 28-29**

**p. 30-31**

**p. 32-33**

**p. 34-35**

**p. 38-39**

**p. 40-41**

p. 48-49

p. 50

p. 52-53

p. 54-55

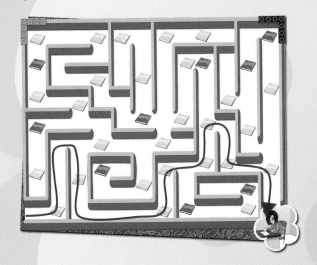